We Sang Across the Sea
The Empire Windrush and Me

Benjamin Zephaniah

ILLUSTRATED BY

Onyinye Iwu

SCHOLASTIC

I was born on the island of Trinidad, in the Caribbean Sea,

There was mum and dad, I had four sisters,

And my four sisters had me.

We Sang Across the Sea
The Empire Windrush and Me

For all children who love to sing,
and children who love listening.
Regardless of your colour or race,
please make this world a better place.
B.Z.

To my mum.
Who sacrificed everything for me.
I love you.
O.I.

Published in the UK by Scholastic, 2022
Euston House, 24 Eversholt Street, London, NW1 1DB
Scholastic Ireland, 89E Lagan Road, Dublin Industrial Estate, Glasnevin, Dublin, D11 HP5F

SCHOLASTIC and associated logos are trademarks and/or
registered trademarks of Scholastic Inc.

Text © Benjamin Zephaniah, 2022
Illustration © Onyinye Iwu, 2022

ISBN 978 07023 1116 1

A CIP catalogue record for this book is available from the British Library.

Any website addresses listed in the book are correct at the time of going to print. However, please
be aware that online content is subject to change and websites can contain or offer content that is
unsuitable for children. We advise all children be supervised when using the internet.

Printed and bound by CPI Group (UK) Ltd, Croydon, CR0 4YY
Paper made from wood grown in sustainable forests and other controlled sources.

1 3 5 7 9 10 8 6 4 2

www.scholastic.co.uk

We loved to play in the sunshine,
The sun shone all the time,
Even when the rains came, the sun was right behind.

One day after playing, as we ate fruits from our trees,
We sat on the veranda enjoying the cool breeze.
We were five girls dreaming of what to do,
When we got older and bigger,
But when it came to me I said,
I want to be a singer.

I just want to sing.
I just want to sing,
Singing songs will help me grow,
I just want the world to know,

Joy is what I bring,
So, I just want to sing.

I started singing on the islands
At shows and carnivals,
If there were no people I would sing to all the animals.

I used to sing in the mornings, I loved to sing at noon,
Singing at night was a great delight,
That's when I sang to the moon.

Then I heard that the Empire Windrush
would sail across the sea,
That ship was sailing to England,
So I told my family.

PASSENGER OPPORTUNITY
TO UNITED KINGDOM

TROOPSHIP 'EMPIRE WINDRUSH'
SAILING 3RD MAY

FARES: CABIN CLASS £48
TROOPDECK . . . £28

ROYAL MAIL LINES, LIMITED
8 PORT ROYAL ST.

I told them of all the things in
England I would like to do,

If I could sing in England
it would be a dream come true.

So, I just want to sing.
I just want to sing,
Singing songs will help me grow,
I just want the world to know,

Joy is what I bring,
So, I just want to sing.

My parents said, 'Good luck, Mona', and 'Take care',
As they waved,
My sisters looked at the great big ship, and they were all amazed.
As the ship left the dock and we started to sail
They all waved goodbye,

I was a little nervous,
    and a bit lonely, and a tear fell from my eye.

There were many on that journey, and they came from many lands,
Many of them were musicians, and they played in many bands.
So when they asked me who I was, and what skills did I bring,
I said, 'My name is Mona Baptiste, and I just love to sing.'

I just want to sing.
I just want to sing,
Singing songs will help me grow,
I just want the world to know,

Joy is what I bring,

So, I just want to sing.

When I arrived in England it was cool,
but then the summer came,
I started singing everywhere, so people
would get to know my name.

I sang in clubs and on radio to get some recognition,
I worked very hard, and soon I even sang on television.

They called me the singing sensation,
    from far across the sea,
My family were proud, and so was I,
    when they talked about me.
I sang in Germany, I sang in France,
    I sang in Ireland too,
But sometimes people still asked me,
    what did I want to do.

I just want to sing.
I just want to sing,
Singing songs will help me grow,
I just want the world to know,

Joy is what I bring,
So, I just want to sing.

Sometimes life was tough, but singing helped me get along,
As a Caribbean girl, sometimes I just had to be quite strong.
Sometimes it could be difficult to just get on the stage,
Sometimes I needed someone to help me turn the page.

I wanted to sing for the whole world,
and I wanted to sing for me,
That's why I got on the Empire Windrush
and sailed across the sea.

So when you think of me remember,
that I fulfilled my dream,
And if you can sing with me I'm sure
that you'll know just what I mean.

I wanted to sing,
I just wanted to sing,
Singing really helped me grow,
So, I wanted the world to know,

I did all that travelling,
Because I just
loved to sing.

Mona Baptiste

Singer and actress Mona Baptiste was born in Port of Spain, Trinidad in 1928. She set sail from Trinidad to England on the Empire Windrush at the age of 20. She sang all around the world, in many languages, appearing in films and on TV shows too. Mona's most well-known song was 'Calypso Blues'. Hugely famous in Europe, Mona lived in Germany for many years before retiring to Ireland, where she passed away in 1993.

Benjamin Zephaniah

The multi-award-winning Dr Benjamin Zephaniah was born and raised in Handsworth, Birmingham in the UK. He is a writer, poet, actor and musician.

Onyinye Iwu

Onyinye Iwu was born in Italy to Nigerian parents and moved to the UK as a teenager. Onyinye is an illustrator, an author, and a former teacher who loves to read.